MERSEYSIDE

POLONIA

Przyjemnej lektury,
zdobywania wiedzy i doświadczeń
życzy Gosia McKane
wraz z Zespołem Merseyside Polonia

„Sztuka jest po to,
by niepokoić, wiedza uspokaja"
Georges Braqwe

Przyjemnej lektury,
zdobywania wiedzy i doświadczeń
wraz z Zespołem Merseyside Polonia

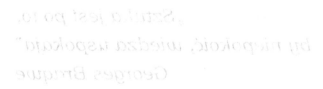

LAND OF GREEN GINGER

Limited Edition
First printing, 2018
Printed in the United Kingdom

ISBN 978-1-902039-32-9

Published by Absolutely Cultured Ltd.
www.absolutelycultured.co.uk

Illustrated by Katy Riddell
Written by Christina Lewis and Katy Fuller
Edited by Maddie Maughan

Designed by Process Black Design

Printed and bound by Bluestorm Design & Marketing

LAND OF GREEN GINGER

Illustrated by Katy Riddell
Written by Christina Lewis and Katy Fuller

PROLOGUE

*There once was a Land that
nobody believed existed.*

And every day people passed by it or around it or over it or through it, but never once saw it or felt it or heard it or knew any person or thing in it.

Until, one day, the Land revealed itself…

The Land was not a land as you or I might think of it. It was not a place with borders and landscapes and laws and customs.

This Land was almost anything and everything you could imagine, whether likely or outlandish. It was every one of the myths and legends and stories you have ever heard or told yourself. It was all of the dreams you've not yet had as well as those which have woken you up laughing or weeping in the middle of the night. It was every person, animal, mythical creature, god and ghost, on every journey, adventure or quest there could be.

*Everything in this Land crackled with a thrilling sense of being outside of the ordinary – **extra**ordinary. But because of this it was unstable and unpredictable and mercurial and tricky. Some would say it was dangerous.*

So it was packed away, shut inside some carefully labelled packing crates and hidden deep underground, far beneath the city of Kingston-upon-Hull.

Was it tucked up to keep it safe, or locked up to keep us safe?

*Whichever the answer, a force like that will not be held fast for long and so came the day that the Land revealed itself - not all of itself, because that would surely have been too much excitement for ordinary people to take in one dose and would likely have resulted in frenzy and panic on the streets of Hull! Instead it revealed itself slowly in a series of **Acts of Wanton Wonder**, across the city and throughout the year of 2017.*

*Perhaps you saw one of these **Acts**? Perhaps you witnessed them all? Perhaps you learned to recognise the signs which showed that another **Act of Wanton Wonder** was about to begin?*

In this book we'll tell of six **Acts** which seeped into the cracks of everyday life to astonish, delight and thrill, and to leave a lasting change on everyone who came into contact with them.

Every **Act** began with the contents of one of the packing crates, but every time what emerged from those crates was wildly different. It was as if each **Act** was a "land" in itself, and each revealed something of the place where it happened.

What stories shall we tell of this Land and of these **Acts of Wanton Wonder**? Not all of the detail of what came to pass, because how could we succeed in describing the sights and the sounds when magic is afoot? Let's talk, instead, of people – ordinary, everyday, decidedly unmagical people – who found their lives altered by the appearance of this Land in one of its many, varied guises.

One last thing, before we begin. The name of this Land?

The Land of Green Ginger

ACT I:
7 ALLEYS

7 Alleys

7 ghost stories on a ghost page
Written in a ghost book
Torn from a ghost page
From the Land of Green Ginger
To the Shores of East Hull
Searching for midnight in the
7th alley portal

Scary Mary was her name,
'Knock Off Ginger' was the game.
The boys would egg each other on,
Ring the doorbell, then they'd run.

Chests bursting, hearts pumping,
Feet pounding, legs jumping,
Over fences, through a ditch,
Running from the scary witch,

Down Preston Road till they reached the drain,
Then back to do it all again.
It was just some fun, just a dare,
Just for kicks, just for the scare,

Just to fill the boring days,
Till something different came their way.
Then, in the middle of their game,
Along that "something different" came…

Two black horses pulled a carriage;
A sign behind read '7 Alleys'.
Fiddlers playing on the back,
Runners and riders dressed in black.

Horses' hooves and bells ringing,
Strange people, eerie singing,
Scrolls tied up with red silk bows,
Passed from the carriage to those below.

As the carriage pulled away,
The boys returned to usual play.
Now Richard's turn to ring the bell;
He turned to scarper – but he fell!

With twisted ankle, knee all scraped,
He barely made it to the gate,
When Scary Mary caught his eye,
And beckoned him to come inside.

Something in her look that day
Meant he dare not disobey.
She washed and patched him up with care,
And told him that she knew their dare.

"You think you're brave," she laughed with glee,
"Young man, you've not a thing on me!
When I was your age, just a scally,
We used to run the 7 Alleys.

"One alley, two alley, three alley, four,
We'd dare ourselves to run one more.
We never found the seventh one,
But searching for it was our fun."

"There's a search on!" Richard cried,
"The scrolls invited us to try."
"Then go!" said Mary, on her feet,
"And bring me tales of who you meet."

He counted down the days from then,
With dreams of alleys opening;
And 'Knock Off Ginger' lost appeal,
Though still up Mary's path they'd steal.

One night in May, when it was dark,
He dragged his friends up to East Park,
Where lights were strung from tree to tree,
And no one guessed what they would see.

"What's this?" his mates scoffed, with a groan.
"We'd have more fun by going home."
"You really think we'll find this alley?
They're baby fairy tales, you wally!"

But then, the ground beneath them moves,
Vibrating with the beat of hooves.
A whinny, bells, the violin;
Smoke and sparks and it begins.

The cart comes down to guide them there,
7 Alleys, 7 dares.
Bombs are dropping, sirens wail,
Bubbles float up, round and pale.

Billowing sails cut through the night,
A harpy, spinning, dressed in white,
And reams of paper fill the air,
As Richard takes the final dare…

The morning's like a world away,
And all the boys are out to play.
But Richard? He's not kicking balls,
Or lobbing tin cans off the wall.

Today he has a place to go –
To Mary's house, to let her know
About the things he saw last night,
The past played out in firelight.

"Come in!" she says, and steps aside,
But Richard hesitates and smiles.
"Come *out!*" he laughs, "You really should.
A bit of sun will do you good."

And so, they sit there, newfound friends;
He tells her how the story ends,
The Alley there before his eyes.
"It sounds amazing," Mary sighs.

He nods, "Then pages fluttered free,
I found a few for you to see.
They're all the same – you see the boar?
I think that's trying to tell us more."

She takes the paper, strokes her chin,
Reads the riddle held within.
"It might be Bransholme," she declares,
"Shall we share a trip out there?"

HULL DAILY MAIL

LEGENDARY GOLD NOSE OF GREEN GINGER FOUND IN CRATE

LUCKY ARTEFACT RE-
DISCOVERED AFTER
PRESUMED LOST

2 FREE

ACT II:
THE GOLD NOSE OF GREEN GINGER

A Gold Nose. A Gold Nose? What does that mean?
Chelsea stood wondering, idly.
Her wares seemed to taunt her, her doorway stood empty,
Yet over the road were people aplenty.

One week ago, her shop full to the rafters,
The hubbub of gossip and chit-chat and laughter,
Then suddenly – nothing. The shop door stopped swinging.
And worse still, her till had completely stopped ringing.

Everywhere round her shone trays of gold treasure,
Waiting for people to buy at their leisure.
Instead something new with a golden glow,
Had taken the shine from her shop window.

It started one Saturday. Out in the centre,
Some kind of procession was starting to enter.
She stuck out her head to see trumpets and pleats,
A riot of colour disrupting the streets.

It looked ceremonial, a grand celebration.
They followed this gold thing with grave dedication.
Bemused, yet in awe, shoppers started to linger,
A whisper began: *"The Gold Nose of Green Ginger?"*

No one quite knew what this new thing was for;
Some talked of legends and ancient folklore.
Chelsea, for certain, just hadn't a clue,
And *her* nose out of joint, wasn't sure what to do.

As days turned to weeks her shop dwindled in trade;
The Gold Nose of Green Ginger was casting a shade.
She'd freely admit she was starting to hate
This odd-shaped gold thing found inside an old crate.

The girls who would always fawn over *her* gold
Were over there now, obsessed with The Nose.
Not a glance at her shop – was she going crazy? –
They were serving up tea and playing with babies!

They hung off the Guardian, talked to The Nose,
Jammed flutes up their nostrils, wore colourful clothes.
They whispered of wishes made true by Nose magic
(Which Chelsea discarded as silly and tragic).

One girl, whom no one had ever heard speak,
Was the first to arrive and the last one to leave.
She helped the small children make noses to wear,
And tidied the shop after craft sessions there.

Yes; something a little bit weird had occurred,
But no one else Chelsea met seemed to concur.
They were drawn to the Nose like moths to a flame,
Going back to its glimmer again and again.

And yet – though she really was loath to admit –
Perhaps it was more than an old counterfeit?
There had to be *something* that made them go there,
But taking her business was more than unfair.

It got to week four and the stories got dafter.
She tried not to meet them with cynical laughter.
But really, she asked, is there no one I know,
Who hasn't had wishes made true by a *Nose?*

So far – and this was on one single day –
She'd heard of arthritis just going away.
A new job, a pools win, an MOT pass,
A long-lost twin sister appearing at last.

It honestly wouldn't surprise me, one day,
To hear a world leader just pop up to say,
"We're pleased to announce that all fighting will cease.
This lucky Gold Nose is the source of World Peace."

And yet, though she scoffed, at the back of her mind,
Was a creeping suspicion she tried hard to hide.
It started to bubble as every day passed,
And Chelsea had even more questions to ask.

There is more to this life than we oft dare to dream,
But luck from a Nose? How on earth can that be?
She couldn't deny it had brought people joy,
So perhaps no matter if real or a toy.

And as the time passed, Chelsea thought more and more,
Watching folk wish on The Nose from her door.
She knew it was nonsense but maybe, just maybe…
Could this silly talisman grant her a baby?

Another day passed with still no sale in sight,
And Chelsea was locking her shop up that night,
When curious thoughts entered into her mind,
And urgently whispered of what she might find.

She pulled down the shutters, stole straight to The Nose,
Creeping and balancing on her tip toes.
Her heartbeat drummed louder than anything there,
But Chelsea was far too excited to care.

Was this really it? She smoothed down her suit.
Not quite like a nose, but more like a… *root?*
Was this really what people revered so much?
She couldn't see anything magic, as such.

Then suddenly, out of the silence, it came.
She listened more closely and heard it again;
The barely-there sound of regular breathing.
She rubbed at her eyes in case she was dreaming.

How long did she stay there? She just couldn't say.
But Chelsea would always remember that day.
For standing alone there with The Gold Nose,
The hope in her belly ignited and rose.

She put pencil to paper and took a deep breath,
Her hand scribbling furiously over the desk.
Then folding it over, felt tension released –
Now she must wait. Will her wish be Unleashed?

HULL DAILY MAIL

LAND OF GREEN GINGER CRATE UNEARTHED IN LONG HILL ALLOTMENT

STRANGE CONTENTS FOUND WITHIN THE CRATE INCLUDED A JAR OF ASHES PERTAINING TO A ONCE CEREMONIAL BURN...

ACT III:
THE LONGHILL BURN

Jimmy Johnson feels adrift,
Although he can't quite pinpoint it.
On the surface, all is good,
Kicking round the neighbourhood.

Sundays, Wednesdays – Five-a-Side,
Teaching kids to weave and dive;
Running round the playing fields,
Wind-burnt cheeks, knees scuffed and peeled.

He picks up odd jobs here and there
(It just depends what's going spare),
And Janet says he's a godsend,
While her bad back is on the mend.

Life ticks on and though it's fine,
Jimmy knows he's biding time.
He often dreams of childhood days:
The endless, stress-free summer haze…

But then, he always had some friends
To knock about with at weekends.
Since Year Ten it's always been
Just him and Laura – lovelorn teens.

He always wanted her to have
As much as possible – that's love –
But now – a twinge of self-pity –
She's gone to university.

One evening, passing by the green,
He sees a quite nostalgic scene.
Kids and adults play together,
A rounders game for sunny weather.

Jimmy watches, hand on chin,
Recalling happy times for him.
He's lost deep in his reverie,
When someone asks if he wants tea.

A person he's not seen till now
Takes his hand and gives a bow.
"I'm from the Firesmiths. How d'you do?
Stay a while and have a brew."

He sees a few more dressed the same,
Joining in the rounders game.
His curiosity is raised:
"What brought you Firesmiths here today?"

"We've been asked to build a fire,
a huge and beautiful Longhill pyre,
The like of which won't be believed,
Out on the Eastmount Playing Fields."

Jimmy lifts the mug and sips;
The tea's like nectar on his lips.
He listens to the voices churn,
The Firesmiths talking of their Burn.

It's been three days since Laura called,
And Jimmy's feeling really bored.
His mother makes him take a walk,
And tries to get her son to talk.

But he's not in the mood for chatter,
Doesn't quite know what's the matter,
When "Whoah!" his mother cries out, turning,
"That massive bonfire, ripe for burning!"

They see those Firesmiths have been grafting,
Building, heaving, layering, crafting.
And now the neighbourhood's alight,
Excited for the Burn tonight.

The Firesmiths gang have one more task,
"What gives you hope?" a helper asks.
Jimmy takes the piece of card,
Holds it tightly, thinking hard.

And somewhere deep within his heart,
He feels a tiny flicker start.
He writes of people brought together,
Longhill memories in all weathers –

Neighbours, friends, community,
The things that make your heart soar free.
He stands back then, in heat-edged dark,
To watch the bonfire in *his* park.

The sun is setting, sky ablaze.
All around him faces gaze.
Waiting for the fire to start,
The flames to reach the central heart.

And as it burns, a crate is lifted,
Offered to this pyre – gifted.
Hoisted up to reach the heart,
And burned until it falls apart.

Jimmy sees what's happening,
That all their hopes are crammed within,
And burning them till black and curled,
Will send them out into the world.

The crowd is whooping, full of cheer,
And songs of Longhill reach his ears.
When the fireworks bang and crack,
A hand is placed on Jimmy's back.

He turns. She meets his eyes and smiles,
"I wanted to come home – surprise!"
In his heart, a warmth ignites,
As Laura's smile beams through the night.

He doesn't know if it's for good,
But something's lifted in his mood.
Their arms entwined, flames dancing high,
They watch the colours paint the sky.

ACT IV:
RE-REDIFFUSION'S VOICE PARK

Agnes could make herself just *disappear*
From the littlest toe to the tip of her ear.
It was a habit she'd come to adopt,
Which ensured that her social life floundered and flopped.

It wasn't because she was rude, not one bit,
But rather she found that her words wouldn't fit;
Instead, she would make herself shrink down so small,
That people who saw her, saw nothing at all.

One day, she was wandering round Walton Street,
Perusing the market for good deals on meat,
When suddenly up popped a man in her path,
A strange apparatus attached to his back.

"We're collecting Hull's voices!" He asked if she'd do it:
"It won't take a moment and there's nothing to it."
"I've nothing to say," she cried, "nothing that matters."
"Don't worry!" he smiled "There's no need to natter."

"Don't think about words – they can't always be found.
Dig deep in your throat and have faith in your sounds."
So, feeling much braver, determined to speak,
She faced the machine and let out a squeak.

Her voice was sucked in, turned to smoke in its case;
She was given a card with a date, time and place.
"When we've gathered enough voices, later this year,
Our Voice Park will open – come lend an ear!"

Fast forward some months since that memorable talk,
And Agnes decides to go out for a walk.
The card has been buried, hidden, forgotten,
And Agnes' voice is not exercised often.

She heads out to Pickering Park on the bus,
The day on the verge of transforming to dusk.
She strolls through the park, book clutched to her chest,
Looking for somewhere deserted to rest.

Then, out of nowhere, she hears "aahs" and "oohs".
The sounds seem to come from the kids' paddling pool.
And something, yes something, is thick in the air.
She doesn't know what it is, why, who or where.

Then all of a sudden, to her great surprise,
She feels like her body's been magnetised;
The pull is insistent, and she's not alone,
And the others who gather clutch cards of their own.

They follow the noises, see lights are pulsating.
Could *this* be the Voice Park they'd all been awaiting?
There stand two people, enveloped in sound,
Inviting them into this sonic playground.

"Good evening and welcome. Come and have fun!
Our colleagues will show you what needs to be done."
They gesture behind them to pods of all sizes,
Spewing out different harmonic surprises.

She doesn't quite notice when dusk turns to night,
Entranced by the noises, enthralled by the lights,
But gradually, watching the others at play,
She plucks up the nerve to hear what they say.

She's up on her tiptoes and down on her knees,
Playing around with the sounds that she hears,
Keeping an ear out for one tiny squeak
Pinched from the market on Walton Street.

She's so busy working her way round the park,
She hasn't quite realised it's now pitch-dark.
But then Agnes spots him, the man from before,
Who extracted her voice by the discount meat stall.

"This is for you," he says, holding a bottle,
"This potion will make your voice work at full throttle.
It's all of the voices we've gathered from Hull,
Distilled to an essence beyond powerful!

"Just uncork the bottle and waft it towards
The place in your throat where you have vocal chords.
Just use a little – though it's personal choice –
Perhaps you desire a huge, booming voice?"

Well, after that, Agnes could hardly object
(Whilst doubting its highly-inflated effect).
She leaves in a rush with no more to discuss,
And she exits the Voice Park to catch the last bus.

It's now three months later and deep in December –
Where is the Agnes who went unremembered?
And held her head low as she walked down the street,
Never daring to raise her eyes up from her feet?

The Voice Park provided a sharp understanding,
That prior to that, she'd been so undemanding.
The times that she'd wanted to roar, cheer and shout,
She'd sat quiet and uttered no words from her mouth.

So, without hesitation, she popped out the cork –
Discarded in haste with the promise of talk.
She paused for a moment, the vial in her hand,
And rubbed every drop on her throat as she'd planned.

(Suffice to say, and you'll know this if you're wise,
When dealing with magic, pay heed to advice.
If Agnes had done so she wouldn't have faced
A voice like a foghorn for thirty-six days.)

But nevertheless, when her vocal chords quietened,
And the Labrador living next door was less frightened,
Agnes felt something shift deep down inside –
Her confidence slowly beginning to rise.

She took a great plunge and signed up for the year,
An extrovert, outgoing, Hull Volunteer.
Now, in her scandalous blue, she stands tall,
And speaking to others holds no fear at all.

ACT V:
MICROPOLIS

For forty years Dave's worked at night,
A watchman on the Springhead site.
The Pumping Station's his domain,
He rules the roost come shine or rain.

He spends his evenings dealing with
Things he shouldn't on his shift;
Cheeky kids and sneaky couples,
Loud teenagers causing trouble.

Nosy parkers, drunken louts,
Dogs he has to chase back out.
"He's quite the jobsworth" people say,
But Dave just likes to keep things safe.

And then, of course, the building rounds,
Making sure it's safe and sound;
Dave prides himself on his inspections,
Settling only for perfection.

His favourite time, generally,
Is when all's done – a cup of tea.
He settles down and writes his findings,
Never really that exciting.

But one thing bugs him on the hour:
A flashing light up in the tower.
He reports it, though it seems,
That no one cares what he has seen.

One night, when Dave is on his rounds,
He hears a sudden crashing sound
Behind a massive stack of boxes.
Pigeons? Rats? Or feral foxes?

He squeezes through a narrow space,
Trips and lands upon his face.
He points his torch beam at the floor:
Some tiny footprints lead next door.

He thinks he must investigate,
Even though it's getting late.
The door creaks open as he's pushing,
Then his blood is really rushing!

Cardboard buildings, ceiling-height,
Fill the room as far as sight.
A tiny city with all features,
Filled with tiny human creatures.

Something catches his attention:
A mini Springhead Pumping Station!
Feeling brave, he puts his face
Against the tiny wrought-iron gates.

And there he is, the tiny Dave,
Cleaning spiders off the gate.
He notices, as streetlamps shine,
The deep-set groove of his frown lines.

"Do I always look that peevish?"
Dave's surprised and slightly sheepish.
He starts to look around in wonder
And sees this city's built from plunder!

Tiny lampposts light this land,
Half the span of Dave's huge hand,
Flickering gently as he tracks
The city through the cardboard stacks.

Dave nips his arm and rubs his eyes –
gives some other things a try –
But when he opens them again,
All he sees is just the same.

A city, with its shops and bars,
Tiny schools and tiny cars.
Dave cannot contain his bliss
At finding this *Micropolis*.

Hours pass, the new day's dawning,
The Pumping Station's finally warming;
Dave's still there, he's mesmerised
By how their world is synchronised.

He notices that every part
Holds all the others at its heart;
They work together, not alone,
And that's just how their world has grown.

He cannot wait to tell the team,
So they can witness what he's seen.
They're quite surprised to hear him rave;
They're much more used to grumpy Dave.

But things don't go quite as he'd hoped;
Before he knows it, he's provoked.
Anticipation far and wide,
And everybody wants inside.

Now he finds himself besieged
By all the horrors that he feared,
But gradually, he must admit,
That people are quite delicate.

They love *Micropolis* just as much
As Dave himself does and, as such,
They want to hear his tale of finding
Such a wonder, there, in hiding.

He lightens up and starts to chat,
Shares his tales and chews the fat.
As weeks go past, to his surprise,
He finally starts to realise;

He quite likes whiling hours away,
Meeting new friends day-to-day.
Perhaps, he thinks, the time has come
To be a happier watchman.

HULL DAILY MAIL

LAND OF GREEN GINGER CRATES APPEAR ON CITY ROOFS

A NUMBER OF CRATES MARKED 'UNLEASHED' HAVE MYSTERIOUSLY APPEARED THROUGH- OUT THE CITY CENTRE

LAND O GREEN GINGER UNLEASHED

Hudgell

OFF THIS WEEK

ACT VI:
LAND OF GREEN GINGER UNLEASHED

Hull is waiting, something's brewing,
Feel it on the air; what's coming?
Potent, indescribable;
Like anything is possible.

A bell chimes out, the sound of hooves,
Under pavements, over roofs.
Whispers, whistles, float on high,
A keening drone, a pensive sigh.

A sense of hidden eyes, looking.
What's this alchemy that's cooking?
Crates have started to appear,
Adding to the atmosphere.

Crates on rooftops, crates in piles,
Crates in doorways, windows, aisles.
As if by magic, on Lowgate –
A simply massive stack of crates.

Marks appear on cobbled streets,
Curious signs beneath the feet.
'Land of Green Ginger', they declaim.
The crates all carry marks the same.

Shoppers swap inquiring glances
At these strange new circumstances.
But it's a truly thrilling air
That's filling Queen Victoria Square.

The noises are more frequent now,
And growing louder by the hour;
A bubbling, boiling energy,
A crackling electricity.

And as the afternoon turns late,
People gather by the crates.
No one can explain quite why,
Except they feel it deep inside.

Like moths that fly into the light;
They simply know tonight's the night.
And then a few becomes a lot,
All gathered round in various spots.

The thickness in the air is growing,
And the crates have started glowing.
Occasionally, they shake and rock,
And people next to them back off.

Whatever's going on, it seems
That all are sharing in the dream,
Where wooden crates just can't contain
What lies within their wooden frame.

Mist and sparkles, smoke and light
Are flowing through the darkening night,
Spilling through the nooks and crannies,
Scaring children, thrilling grannies!

Then all at once the crates burst open
In a booming, bright explosion.
Flames and sparks go flying high,
Illuminating all the sky.

People marvel, point and gape,
As things inside make their escape.
Birds twirl free alongside pages,
Glitter rains on upturned faces.

Then the fanfare, as they come,
Accompanied by beating drums:
Giants, high as any steeple,
Flanked by scores of tiny people.

Scattered all around their feet,
Tiny footprints in the street.
A huge winged horse, as dark as night,
Pulls a carriage filled with light.

Stags and wolves are running fast,
A woman with a grinning mask,
Giant toadstools, hares leap free,
As red smoke clouds their gleeful spree.

A Gold Nose sniffs its way around
As people stand and watch, spellbound;
Fire, wonder, magic, song,
Drive the rabbling, manic throng,

And then, there comes the strangest thing –
Everybody starts to *sing*.
They look and reach and find each other,
Struck by urgent, sudden wonder.

Grabbing hands and spinning round,
The street's a blur of joyful sounds.
Laughing, whooping, cheering, twirling,
Round in rapture all go whirling.

Older folk with younger ones,
Giddy toddlers with their mums,
Richard, Chelsea, Mary, Jimmy,
Dave and Agnes start to shimmy.

The wolves rear up and bay a tune
Against the shining silver moon.
Confetti floats and sparks rain down,
Covering all of Hull's old town.

Hand in hand and arm in arm,
Hull's an effervescent storm
Of love and wonder, life and joy,
For men and women, girls and boys.

And nevermore will life be dull.
Forevermore for those from Hull
These wanton, wondrous Acts will linger:
Memories of Land of Green Ginger.

EPILOGUE

There once was a Land that nobody believed existed. And every day people passed by it or around it or over it or through it, but never once saw it or felt it or heard it or knew any person or thing in it.

Until, one day, the Land revealed itself…

And because of that, people began to believe and behave in all sorts of strange and wonderful ways. They wanted to leave work and play and wonder and be part of this amazing world. They wanted to share it with friends and family and neighbours and visitors and strangers.

And because of that, this real world changed too. The status quo was not so fixed and people questioned things they had always accepted.

And then, one day, the Land started to fade away and things began to return to something a little more akin to normal. But traces and reminders and changes and memories remained.

Perhaps, one day, the Land of Green Ginger will return, but for now, our world is a little more like it.

ACKNOWLEDGEMENTS

To the artists who created the live Acts of Wanton Wonder. You are all magicians:

Act I: **7 Alleys** by **Periplum**

Act II: **The Gold Nose of Green Ginger** by **Joshua Sofaer**

Act III: **The Longhill Burn** by **And Now:**

Act IV: **Re-Rediffusion's Voice Park** by **Aswarm**

Act V: **Micropolis** by **The McGuires**

Act VI: **Land of Green Ginger Unleashed** by **Macnas** in collaboration with **And Now:**

To Simon Sharkey who helped to create the *Land of Green Ginger* and keep it alive when it threatened to evaporate.

In memory of Bill Mitchell, of Wildworks, who gifted the phrase "Acts of Wanton Wonder".

To the Hull 2017 Volunteers who become *Land of Green Ginger* Ambassadors.

To the Green Ginger team who lived, breathed and dreamed this project. You know who you are.

BACKGROUND

Hull 2017's groundbreaking community engagement project, *Land of Green Ginger*, invited Hull's residents to immerse themselves in a magical citywide story, inspired by and celebrating the spirit of Hull.

Land of Green Ginger was presented as a series of events or Acts of Wanton Wonder, united under an overarching narrative. The individual Acts were developed and delivered with artists who worked both independently and in collaboration to bring new kinds of art and culture into the neighbourhoods outside the city centre.

Six Acts of Wanton Wonder transformed communities across the city into places of wonder, delight, magic and possibility.

This book is the seventh and final Act of the *Land of Green Ginger*.

It has been delivered to residents and schools across the city as a record of the project that took place and as a keepsake for the people whose lives were touched by the magic of *Land of Green Ginger*.

Land of Green Ginger was delivered and produced by Hull 2017, the company which delivered the UK City of Culture 2017 programme and now continues as permanent organisation **Absolutely Cultured**.

Land of Green Ginger was made possible by support from the 80 partners of Hull 2017, but in particular by the support from:

Supported using public funding by
ARTS COUNCIL ENGLAND

LOTTERY FUNDED

NHS
Hull Clinical Commissioning Group